THE SCRIBNER
RADIO MUSIC LIBRARY

Edited by
ALBERT E. WIER

VOLUME IV
GRAND OPERA EXCERPTS
. . .
PIANO

NEW YORK
CHARLES SCRIBNER'S SONS

COPYRIGHT, 1931, 1946, BY CHARLES SCRIBNER'S SONS

Printed in the United States of America

THE SCRIBNER RADIO MUSIC LIBRARY

VOLUME IV—EXCERPTS FROM FAMOUS GRAND OPERAS

TABLE OF CONTENTS—TITLES

THE SCRIBNER RADIO MUSIC LIBRARY

VOLUME IV—EXCERPTS FROM FAMOUS GRAND OPERAS

TABLE OF CONTENTS—COMPOSERS

A Guide Through Volume IV

THE volumes of the SCRIBNER RADIO MUSIC LIBRARY are devoted entirely to compositions which are heard constantly over the great broadcasting chains—played by orchestras, chamber music organizations or instrumental soloists; sung by choral organizations or by vocal soloists. Each of the nine volumes contains only the choicest and most popular of its particular type of music.

This volume is devoted entirely to excerpts, arranged for the piano, from famous grand operas which are constantly heard over the radio in both complete and incomplete form. Grand opera as a whole divides itself naturally into schools under different nationalities, and we will first give our attention to the many Italian operas which are to be found in this volume because of their popularity with the radio audience.

ITALIAN GRAND OPERAS

First comes Bellini's **Norma**, containing the famous "Casta Diva" aria so exquisitely rendered by Lilli Lehmann, and the stirring "Grand March"; then Donizetti's **Lucia**, founded on Sir Walter Scott's novel, "The Bride of Lammermoor," and containing the famous sextette we hear so often over the air; it would be indeed a mistake to omit Rossini's **William Tell**, his most serious effort in the operatic field, well known to the radio music lover through its overture. The strains from **Mefistofele**, by Arigo Boito, a famous librettist as well as composer, are often heard, and both the "Dance of the Hours" and the aria "Cielo é Mar" from Ponchielli's **La Gioconda** are radio favorites. Giuseppe Verdi, considered by many authorities the greatest of Italian opera composers, is well represented in this volume by excerpts from **Aïda,** a tale of love and hate in ancient Egypt; **La Forza del Destino,** in which there is a magnificent tenor and baritone duet often broadcast; **Rigoletto,** teeming with radio favorites, such as "La Donna é Mobile" and the famous "Quartet"; **La Traviata**, with its exhilarating "Drinking Song," and **Il Trovatore**, containing the ever-popular "Miserere" and "Anvil Chorus." From the more modern Italian school we have selected Puccini's **Le Villi** with its bizarre "La Tregenda" dance; then there is Leoncavallo's **I Pagliacci**, from which we are constantly hearing some tenor sing the plaintive "Vesti la Giubba"; and Mascagni's **Cavalleria Rusticana**, the intermezzo from which is very naturally constantly heard as it is unquestionably one of the most popular pieces of music ever written.

FRENCH GRAND OPERAS

The operas of Gluck are included in the French school even although he was not a native son; in this volume you will find excerpts from perhaps the most beautiful of his works, **Orfeo e Eurydice,** from which we often hear the exquisite aria, "I Have Lost My Eurydice"; Herold's **Zampa** is known to us all through its liltingly tuneful overture; the spectacular grand operas of Meyerbeer are represented by selections from **Les Huguenots** with its impressive "Benediction of the Poniards," and **Le Prophéte** with its flashing "Coronation March." Two operas from the pen of Ambroise Thomas claim attention through their radio popularity—**Mignon,** with its exquisite soprano aria, "Know'st Thou That Fair Land?" and **Raymond,** which survives entirely because of its brilliant overture. It has always seemed a pity that Georges Bizet passed away almost immediately after he was successful with **Carmen,** for it is quite probable that he would have conceived many more lasting melodies such as the "Habanera" and the "Toreador Song"; Gounod's **Faust** contains many melodies popular with the radio audience, which also highly approves of the waltz aria in his **Romeo and Juliet**. Jules Massenet, composer of more than seventy operas, most of which are no longer staged, is represented in this volume by selections from **Le Cid** (a musical drama of Spain in the days when it was conquered by the Moors) and **Manon**, the libretto for which was drawn from the same source as Puccini's "Manon Lescaut." Last, but not least among the French operas, is Saint-Saëns' **Samson and Delilah** with its beautiful contralto aria, "My Heart at Thy Sweet Voice," and the graphic "Bacchanale."

GERMAN GRAND OPERAS

In the field of German opera Mozart's **Magic Flute** has many airs familiar to the radio audience by reason of their melodic beauty; Carl Maria von Weber also has two operas best known through their overtures—**Der Freischütz** and **Oberon**. We are constantly hearing the overture as well as songs from Flotow's **Martha**, an opera indissolubly associated with the Irish air, "The Last Rose of Summer." Richard Wagner—accorded the same position in German opera (or music drama) as Verdi of the Italian School—is represented in this volume by excerpts from **The Flying Dutchman**, founded on a tale which always intrigued the master; **Lohengrin**, strains from which are heard every day over the air; **Tannhäuser**, with its impressive "Grand March" and seductive "Evening Star"; **The Mastersingers**, in which the "Prize Song" is a well-known favorite with the radio audience; and **Parsifal**, with its sombre melodies always heard around Eastertide.

RUSSIAN GRAND OPERAS

Russian composers entered the field of opera hundreds of years after other nations, but that has not prevented their conceiving works which are both remarkable and original. Borodin's musical tale of the Russian steppes, **Prince Igor**, contains a number of characteristic dances which are constantly played by orchestras; Moussorgsky's **Boris Godounov** is often heard in orchestral selection; Tschaikowsky's **Eugene Onégin** contains a waltz entr'acte, also an orchestral favorite. Probably the greatest of Russian opera composers is Rimsky-Korsakow; this volume contains selections from **Sadko** with its universally popular "Song of India," **Le Coq d'Or**, containing the equally beloved "Hymn to the Sun," and **The Snow Maiden**, from which the sprightly "Dance of the Tumblers" is an orchestral favorite with the radio audience. This volume also contains excerpts from Rimsky-Korsakow's **Sheherazade**. This, of course, is not an opera but an orchestral suite—its popularity is so great, however, with the radio music lover that it deserves an especial place of honor.

MISCELLANE-OUS GRAND OPERAS

One of the most popular overtures we hear over the radio is that composed for **The Bartered Bride**, by Smetana; the Hungarian composer, Carl Goldmark, is well known to the radio audience through his **Queen of Sheba** in which there are many favorite airs. The Irish composer, Michael Balfe, has written enduringly in **The Bohemian Girl**, as has William Vincent Wallace in **Maritana**. Selections from all these four operas, comprising melodies well known to every radio music lover, are to be found in this volume.

Aïda
Selected Melodies

G. Verdi

Andantino (Heav'nly Aïda)

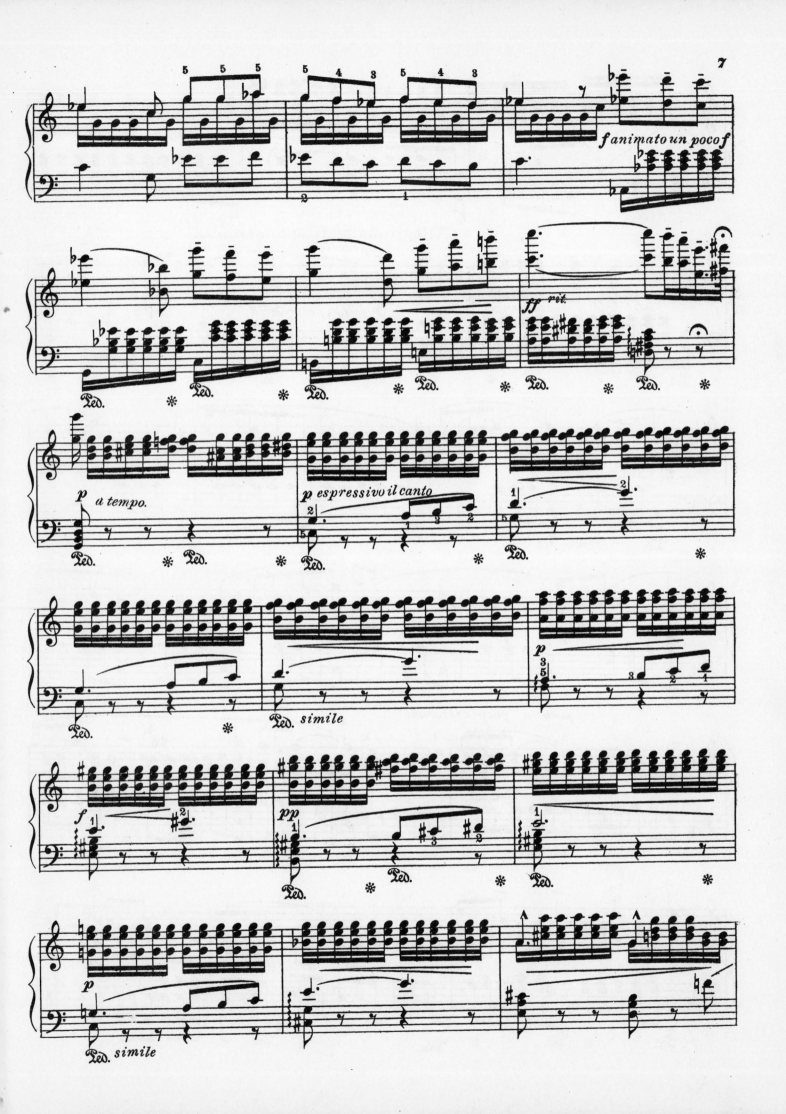

Allegro animato (O Love Immortal)

9

Allegro moderato (Triumphal March)

The Bartered Bride

Selected Melodies

Fr. Smetana

Andantino (Love Duet)

March tempo (Comedian's March)

Maestoso

The Bohemian Girl
Selected Melodies

M. W. Balfe

Larghetto cantabile (When Other Lips And Other Hearts)

Andantino (I Dreamt I Dwelt In Marble Halls)

Moderato (A Soldier's Life)

Boris Godounov
Selected Melodies

M. Moussorgsky

Moderato con grazia (Chorus of Maidens)

Moderato non troppo allegro e sempre capricioso (Marina's Song)

Andante (Duet - Act III)

Andantino (Death of Boris)

Moderato

Meno mosso

Allegro Moderato (Greeting to Boris)

Norma
Selected Melodies

V. Bellini

Andante (Dearest Norma)

Ped. simile

Ped.   *   Ped.   *

rall.

pp

Ped.   *

morendo

Ped.   * Ped.   *   Ped.   *

Maestoso (Druid Chorus)

p

con Pedal

Ped.   *

Tempo di Marcia (March)

Carmen
Selected Melodies

G. Bizet

Con moto (Toreador Song)

con Ped.

40

Tempo di Marcia

ben macato

con Ped.

(Toreador's March)
brillante

Ped. simile

The Magic Flute
Selected Melodies

W. A. Mozart

Andantino (A Bird Charmer am I)

Andantino (Among Those Who Love.)

Allegro Moderato

Le Prophéte

Selected Melodies

G. Meyerbeer

50

Tempo di marcia, molto maestoso (Coronation March)

Zampa
Selected Melodies

Louis Herold

Allegro vivace (Overture)

Moderato (Ballade)

54

Allegro vivace (Finale-Overture)

p scherzando

con Ped. ad lib.

molto rit.

Cavalleria Rusticana

Selected Melodies

P. Mascagni.

Andante Sostenuto
(Siciliana)

Allegretto (Whip Song)

Andante sostenuto (Intermezzo)

Le Cid
Selected Melodies

J. Massenet

Allegro Brillante (Aragonaise)

66

Der Freischütz
Selected Melodies

C. M. von Weber

Valse moderato (Waltz Melody)

Con Pedal

ten

Molto vivace (Huntsmen's Chorus)

Le Coq d'Or

Selected Melodies

N. Rimsky-Korsakow

Allegro moderato

Faust

Selected Melodies

C. Gounod

Tempo di Marcia. (Soldiers' Chorus)

Mouvement de Valse. (Kermesse Waltz)

Allegretto. (Flower Song)

Andante. (Love Duet)

Adagio. (Duet "O Moonlight")

Moderato maestoso. ("Angels Rare, Angels Radiant")

Eugene Onègin

Selected Melodies

P. Tschaikowsky

Tempo di Valse (Entr'acte Waltz)

Orfeo

Selected Melodies

C. W. Von Gluck

Moderato con espressione   (I have lost my Eurydice)

Lento dolcissimo (Ballet)

Allegro (The Triumph of Love)

Più Allegro

sempre ff

The Huguenots

Selected Melodies

G. Meyerbeer

Allegro con moto (Banquet Chorus)

Maestoso (Benediction of the Poniards)

La Gioconda

Selected Melodies

A. Ponchielli

Moderato (Dance of the Hours)

(Entrance of the Hours of the Day)

(Entrance of the Hours of the Night)

p espressivo

Hansel and Gretel

Selected Melodies

E. Humperdinck

Moderato (Children's Prayer)

Tranquillo (O Magic Castle)

110

La Forza del Destino

Selected Melodies

G. Verdi

Andante sostenuto (In this Solemn hour)

Allegro moderato (Leonora's Aria _ Act II)

Lucia di Lammermoor

Selected Melodies

G. Donizetti

118

Moderato (Happy Bridal Day)

Lohengrin
Selected Melodies

R. Wagner

Moderato (Bridal Chorus)

Allegro moderato (Introduction Act III)

sempre *f*

Ped. ✿ Ped. ✿

Ped. ✿ Ped.

ff

✿ Ped. ✿ Ped. ✿

Ped. ✿ Ped. ✿ Ped. ✿

ritard.

Ped. ✿ Ped. ✿ Ped. ✿

Manon

Selected Melodies

J. Massenet

Andantino espressivo (Barcarolle)

En animant peu a peu

Andante cantabile

Allegro

Maritana
Selected Melodies

W. V. Wallace

Tempo Marcia (Let Me Like A Soldier Fall)

Allegro molto (Scenes That Are Brightest)

Martha
Selected Melodies

F. von Flotow

Allegro moderato (Ah! So Pure)

Allegretto

Larghetto (Last Rose Of Summer)

The Mastersingers of Nürnberg

Selected Melodies

R. Wagner

Maestoso (Entrance March of the Mastersingers)

Allegro assai (Finale Act I.)

Piu stretto

Mignon
Selected Melodies

A. Thomas

Tempo di Bolero (Titania's Song)

(Know'st Thou That Fair Land?)

Allegretto moderato (Gavotte)

The Flying Dutchman

Selected Melodies

R. Wagner

Allegretto (Spinning Chorus)

Allegro

Vivace (Finale, Sinking of the Ship.)

Mefistofele
Selected Melodies

A. Boito

Andante (Duet - Act IV)

I Pagliacci

Selected Melodies

R. Leoncavallo

Vivace (Ballatella)

Andante (Vesta la glubba)

Parsifal

Selected Melodies

R. Wagner

Lento (Flower Girl Song)

(March of the Holy Grail)

Lento e solenne

Prince Igor
Selected Melodies

A. Borodin

Allegro (Polish Dance)

Raymond
Selected Melodies

Ambroise Thomas

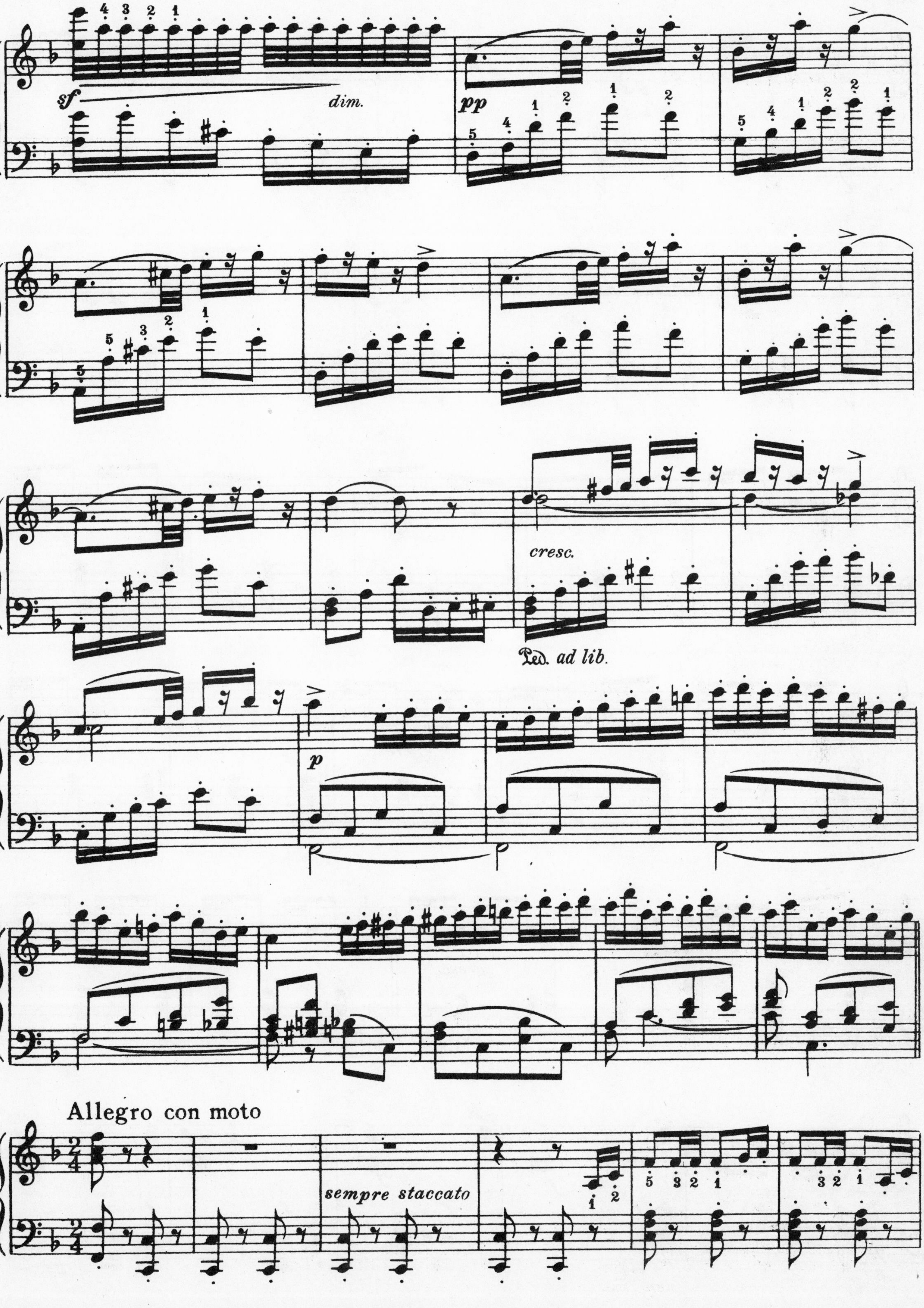
sf
dim.
pp
cresc.
Ped. ad lib.
p
Allegro con moto
sempre staccato

con Ped.

The Queen of Sheba

Selected Melodies

K. Goldmark

Allegretto **(Ballet music)**

Le Villi

Selected Melodies

G. Puccini

Allegro (La Tregenda)

Romeo and Juliet
Selected Melodies

Allegretto vivace (Waltz Aria)

Charles Gounod

Allegretto (Love Duet)

198

Samson and Delilah

Selected Melodies

Andante (My heart at thy sweet voice)

C. Saint Saëns

200

Poco piu lento

Allegro moderato

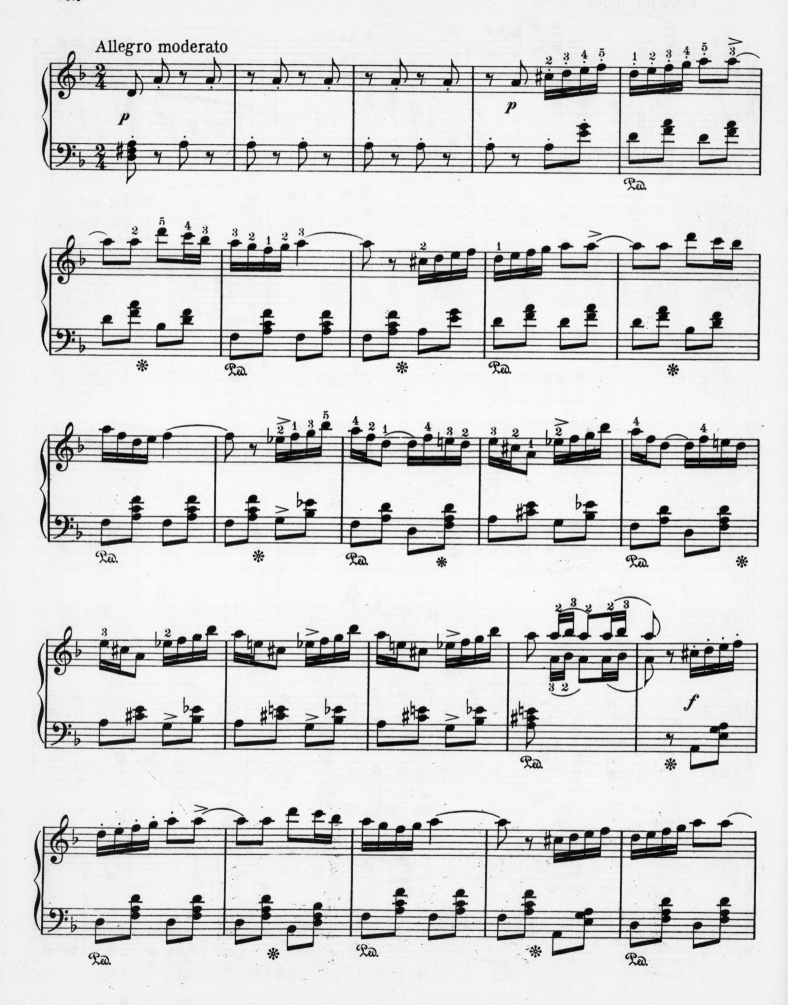

Oberon
Selected Melodies

C. M. von Weber

Andante con moto (Song of the Mermaids)

poco rallent.

Allegro con fuoco **Finale-Overture**

Rigoletto.
Selected Melodies

Giuseppe Verdi

Allegretto. (Ev'ry Flower)

Allegro moderato. (Dearest Name)

210

(Donna é Mobile.)

Ped. ✻ Ped. ✻ Ped. ✻ Ped. ✻ simile

The Snow Maiden
(Dance of the Tumblers)

N. Rimsky - Korsakow

Sheherazade
Selection

N. Rimsky Korsakow, Op.35

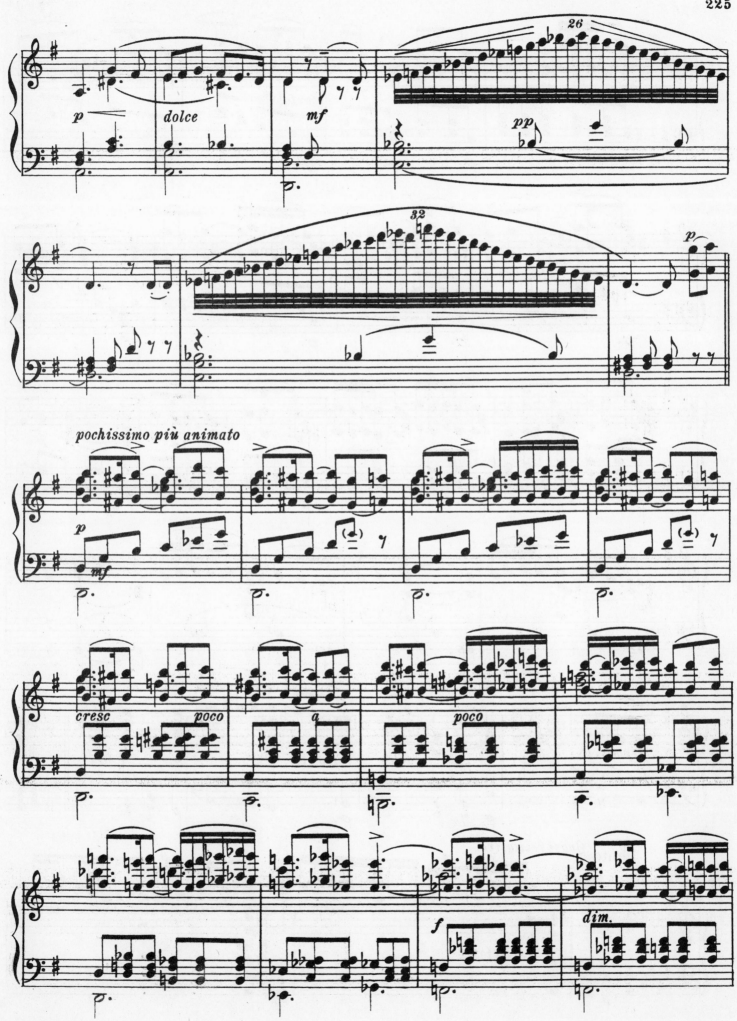

Sadko
Selected Melodies

Andantino (Song of India)

N. Rimsky-Korsakow

William Tell

Selected Melodies

G. Rossini

Ped.   *   Ped. simile

Ped. * Ped. *

Ped. * Ped. * simile

Ped. * Ped. *

Ped. * Ped. *

dim. e rit.

Ped. * Ped. * Ped. * Ped. *

Allegretto (Ballet Music)

234

La Traviata
Selected Melodies

Giuseppe Verdi

Andantino (Ah!'Twas Him)

238

Allegretto (Drinking Song)

Il Trovatore
Selected Melodies

Giuseppe Verdi

Allegro (Anvil Chorus)

tutta forza

Andante sostenuto (Miserere)

Allegro mod^{to} maestoso
(Soldiers March)

Tannhäuser
Selected Melodies

Richard Wagner

Andante maestoso (Pilgrims' Chorus)

249

Andantino (Evening Star)

Kunihild
Prelude to Act III

Cyrill Kistler

Lento *Con dolore*